JULIEN NEEL

DOWN IN THE DUMP

ENGLISH TRANSLATION
BY ROS AND CHLOE SCHWARTZ

 USHARP COMICS

First published in 2006
under the title *Le Cimetière des Autobus*
in the original French by
Editions Glénat
BP 177
38008 Grenoble Cedex.

This English translation published
in 2008 by Usharp Comics,
an imprint of Highland Books Ltd
2 High Pines, Knoll Road
Godalming GU7 2EP
England.

English translation: © 2008 by Ros and Chloë Schwartz

Author's website: www.neelcartoons.com
ISBN-13: 978 1 905496 12 9
ISBN-10: 1-905496-12-5
Printed in Belgium for Usharp Comics by Lesaffre.

9

TEMPORARY PUBLIC TRANSPORT VEHICLE POUND

A BUS CEMETERY

RIGHT OPPOSITE WHERE I LIVE

INSTEAD OF TRISTAN'S BLOCK OF FLATS...

...ALL KNOCKED DOWN

NO MORE TRISTAN

TRISTAN, YOU KNOW, THE BOY WHO...

...WENT TO LIVE IN ANOTHER CITY

... AND WHO I LOVED, AND THEN NEVER HEARD FROM AGAIN...

NOT A PEEP

I DON'T KNOW WHY

I...

WELL...

THERE'S THIS OTHER BOY...

PAUL

WHO I MET AT MY GRANDMA'S

BUT WE WEREN'T IN LOVE

I MEAN, I DON'T THINK SO

IT'S JUST THAT HE WAS LESS...

I MEAN MORE

OR IT'S THE HOLIDAYS THAT THREW—

ME AND TRISTAN, I MEAN

NO, I MEAN, NO, FOR EXAMPLE MY MUM...

...AND RICHARD

OUR NEIGHBOUR...

THE OTHER ONE

WELL, THEY'RE...

BAM

AN ITEM

IN SPITE OF HORATIO HIGGIN-BOTTOM

HEE HEE!

THEY'VE EVEN KNOCKED DOWN THE WALL BETWEEN OUR FLATS

A BIT OF A SHOCK

ON THE FIRST DAY OF TERM TOO

PHAW, AND THEN GOING BACK TO SCHOOL, WAAAOH...

THERE WAS THE BUST UP WITH MINA

I DON'T EVEN KNOW IF WE'RE STILL FRIENDS

I DUNNO, ALLTHIS STUFF, ITS LIKE.....

I FEEL SORT OF ...

ER.....

HOW CAN I EXPLAIN

CONFUSED?

THAT'S IT !

RENT!

OOOOH, FANCY THAT! MRS POOTER!

HOW NICE TO SEE YOU

WHAT A LUCKY COINCIDENCE BECAUSE....

...ABOUT THE RENT

—LISTEN, THIS'LL MAKE YOU LAUGH...

YOU KNOW ABOUT MY BOOK... WELL IT'S OUT...

THE THING IS, ABOUT THE MONEY ...

HAVE YOU HEARD OF JK ROWLING

THAT MEANS THAT IT MAY BE THAT ONE DAY...

RENT!

YES YES YES YES

LOOK, THERE'S THIERRY HENRI!

WHERE? WHERE?

DRAT! SHE'S TRICKED ME AGAIN!

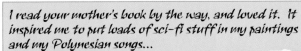 Aloha friend! As we said we'd write and all that, here goes...

I shan't bore you with school stuff. As usual, some morons make fun of me, and as usual, I don't give a toss...

I read your mother's book by the way, and loved it. It inspired me to put loads of sci-fi stuff in my paintings and my Polynesian songs...

My South-Sea island women have astronaut helmets, there are extra-terrestrial crabs and cosmic vehicles overgrown with jungle plants...

The talisman carvings are traces of visitors from ancient times: ocean and cosmos melt into each other. I wish you could see it all!

I'd like to watch the shooting sea stars with you...

PAUL...

15

HEY, I KNOW. LET'S PUT ON SOME CHEESY MUSIC AND DANCE?

YEAH... NAH

WELL THEN LET'S MAKE A LIST OF GIRLS AND GUYS AND THEN PAIR THEM OFF

THAT'D BE A LAUGH

PHWAH. HEY, WE'RE NOT ELEVEN ANY MORE

LET'S JUST GO ON WATCHING VIDEOS

BIDIBIDIBIDI

HI?

?

HELLO-OH

17

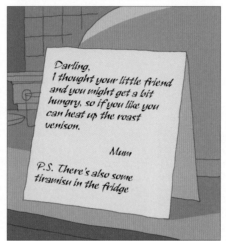

YEAH SO YOU SEE I BROKE UP WITH HIM COS HE WAS TOO HEAVY. YOU KNOW LIKE WITH HIS MATES HE ACTED ALL HARD AND THEN ROUND HIS PARENTS HE WAS A COMPLETE WIMP. I MEAN PSYCHOLOGICALLY HE WASN'T FOR ME. I FOUND HIM REALLY HYPOCRITICAL AND I'M LIKE, WELL, I'M NOT LIKE THAT, LIKE I'M IN YOUR FACE, NOT AFRAID TO SAY WHAT I THINK—DON'T GIVE A TOSS WHAT SOCIETY WILL THINK—I WON'T TOE THE LINE OR HAVE ANYTHING TO DO WITH THEIR ROTTEN DOSH...

THEY CAN'T HANDLE REBELS LIKE ME, CHE GUEVARA OR AVRIL LAVIGNE

MUSKAR WAS A WISE KING WHO LIVED PEACEFULLY ALONGSIDE HIS NEIGHBOURS...

...THE COUNTRY PROSPERED. HE DIED IN 1168, MUCH TO THE SORROW OF HIS SUBJECTS. HIS ELDEST SON SUCCEEDED HIM AS MUSKAR II. HE DID NOT WIELD HIS FATHER'S AUTHORITY, SO DISORDER AND ANARCHY SOON ERODED THAT PROSPERITY...

ANARCHY RULES, YEAH!

YEAH SO YOU SEE GUYS DON'T UNDERSTAND ANYTHING ABOUT GIRLS' PSYCHOLOGY LIKE THEY'RE ALWAYS LIKE "YEAH GIRLIES HOWS ABOUT IT" AND THEY'VE GOT NO RESPECT YOU KNOW LIKE...

...AND TO BE HONEST, I WANT RESPECT FOR HOW I AM, RIGHT? BUT LIKE COS I'M DIFFERENT AND NOT HOW THEY WANT ME THAT PISSES THEM OFF IN THEIR COSY LITTLE LIVES WHERE MONEY'S THE ONLY THING THAT MATTERS ...

WELL I DON'T GIVE A TOSS, RIGHT...

HEY!

I NEED A HUG, PUSS

SORRY ...

?

iiiiik

PHWOAH ...

20

IT'S AS IF THE THINGS, THE PEOPLE, AROUND ME ARE GRADUALLY BECOMING HAZY...

I CAN'T FOCUS MY MIND ON ANYTHING, THE WORLD IS IMMATERIAL...

NO MORE BUMPS, NO UPS AND NO DOWNS, EVERYTHING'S FLAT...

I CAN SPEND HOURS STARING AT A CRACK IN THE CEILING, BUT I CAN'T READ A BOOK FOR MORE THAN A FEW SECONDS...

I DON'T KNOW IF OTHER PEOPLE ARE TURNING INTO GHOSTS...

... OR WHETHER IT'S ME WHO IS GRADUALLY TURNING INTO MY SHADOW...

SO INSUBSTANTIAL THAT I FEEL AS THOUGH I'M FLOATING...

LIGHT ...

SO LIGHT...

WOW

GOTH BRACELETS

WITH SPIKES

SOOO COOL

WHEN I WAS A KID I DREAMED OF HAVING ONE LIKE THAT

BUT MY PARENTS, DUNGSHILL, AND ALL THAT...

A SPIKED WRISTBAND, PLEASE

WITH DOUBLE SPIKES

AN EXCELLENT CHOICE, SIR

HEY NO! NO! NO!

HAPPY CHRISTMAS!

HEY, NO—IT'S RIDICULOUS. IT'S...

IT'S ... IT'S COOOL!

WHA! IT REALLY MAKES ME FEEL POWERFUL...

SSSH: RENT...

RENT?

YEAAAAAH!

LORD HELP ME!

HEY!

PFFFFF ...

HEY, YOU'RE A GUY, SUPPOSE THERE'S THIS GIRL YOU MEET ON HOLIDAY, SUPPOSE...

RIGHT, YEAH?

AND LIKE SHE'S JUST A FRIEND RIGHT, BUT SUPPOSE AFTER SHE GOES BACK HOME, YOU WRITE HER THIS LETTER...

A LETTER? WHAT KIND OF LETTER?

UM... A LETTER: DEAR THINGY, HOW ARE YOU AND ALL THAT STUFF...

YEAH, RIGHT, SUPPOSING... SO?

AND THE GIRL LIKE SHE DOESN'T WRITE BACK FOR SEVERAL MONTHS

WHOAH, THEN SHE'S STUPID, ISN'T SHE?

NO, NO, SHE'S NOT STUPID, IT'S COS SHE'S SCARED STIFF AND SHE'S AFRAID OF WRITING REALLY BORING STUFF THAT'LL MAKE HIM THINK SHE'S DUMB...

ANYWAY

SHE DOESN'T ANSWER BUT AT CHRISTMAS YOU SEND HER A CARD ALL THE SAME...

WELL IT'S REALLY NICE OF ME TO DO THAT IF SHE DIDN'T REPLY THE FIRST TIME...

YEAH, THAT'S WHAT THE GIRL THINKS TOO, THAT YOU'RE REALLY NICE AND THIS TIME SHE MUST WRITE BACK OTHERWISE SHE'LL LOSE YOUR FRIENDSHIP...

BUT THE THING IS SHE DOESN'T KNOW HOW TO EXCUSE HERSELF FOR NOT WRITING BACK THE FIRST TIME...

ANYWAY, SHE FINALLY REPLIES:

DEAR FRIEND,
I'M SORRY I DIDN'T ANSWER YOUR FIRST LETTER, I HAD LOADS OF PROBLEMS WITH THE MAFIA, TWO OF MY FINGERS GOT BROKEN AND STUFF ... ANYWAY, THEY'RE BETTER NOW, HAPPY CHRISTMAS AND BEST WISHES...

HM, I DON'T THINK HER MAFIA STORY IS VERY BELIEVABLE

THAT'S WHAT I THOUGHT ... I HAD THIS OTHER IDEA ABOUT BEING KIDNAPPED BY ALIENS...

WHAT TYPE OF ALIENS?

RiiiTCH!

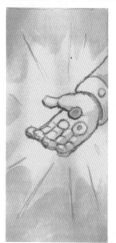

THIEF! LAZY HIPPIE!

... surprise! ... boots always dreamed of!

you not happy?

ER ...

me too surprise for you

you're going to be A FATHER

26

HEY

WHAT?

NEXT LESSON

WHAT THE?

WE'LL SKIP IT

WHAT? ER... UM...

YES
OK
YES

I KNOW A GOOD HIDING PLACE

ONE COFFEE

ER...
ME TOO

THAT GUY PAUL WROTE TO ME AND I... I CAN'T GET IT TOGETHER TO WRITE

HOLD ON, GUYS YOU KNOW, THEY'RE ALL THE SAME...

...LIKE ME, FOR EXAMPLE, I BROKE UP WITH THE GUY WHO DID HENNA TATTOOS, LIKE HE WAS TOO SCREWED UP YOU KNOW, AND LIKE I DON'T GIVE A TOSS ABOUT HIS PROBLEMS YOU KNOW, I DUNNO, BUT WHEN YOU LOOK AT WHAT'S GOING ON IN THE WORLD, EVEN IN YOUR OWN STREET, IT'S SCARY...

IT'S LIKE THE AMERICANS. THEY'RE LIKE TOO MUCH LIKE THEY BELIEVE THEY'RE MASTERS OF THE UNIVERSE WITH THEIR FILTHY MONEY, WHEREAS ACTUALLY THEY SELL ARMS TO CONTROL OIL, BUT IN ACTUAL FACT THEY'RE COMPLETELY SUPERFICIAL.

AND YOU KNOW, ME, I FIND INJUSTICE EVEN MORE UNBEARABLE THAN POVERTY, YOU KNOW, AND THAT'S WHY I DON'T WANT TO BE A SHEEP AND GO AND WORK IN A FACTORY, YOU KNOW. AND THAT'S WHAT WINDS THEM UP, THE BOURGEOISIE, IT'S BECAUSE I'M SO NOT IN THE SYSTEM...

JUST SHUT YOUR TRAP!

ER...

I...I...

KSHLUNK
KSHLUNK

Bip Bip
Bip

HELLO?

MUM?

HELL-OO?

WHAT DO YOU MEAN YOU CAN'T HEAR ANYTHING?

THE OTHER WAY ROUND!

HOLD THE RECEIVER THE OTHER WAY ROUND!

ALL RIGHT NOW?

THAT'S BETTER

ARE YOU WELL

OH ARTHRITIS

YES YES

THAT'S A NUISANCE, YES

OH YES, THAT TOO, YES

AND YOU'VE GOT YOUR VARICOSE VEINS OF COURSE...

HAVE YOU BEEN TO THE DOCTOR'S?

YES, OF COURSE I REMEMBER HORATIO HIGGINBOTTOM...

WHAT?

NO, YOU'RE NOT STILL HARPING ON ABOUT HIM, PUH-LEASE!

RIGHT, WELL, YOU KNOW MY BOOK THAT I WROTE...

WELL IT'S OUT

YES

WHAT?

I DON'T GIVE A DAMN ABOUT MRS HONEYDEW'S GRANDSON AND HIS ENGINEERING DEGREE!

I'VE WRITTEN A BOOK FOR GOODNESS SAKE!

RIGHT WELL YOU CAN CONGRATULATE HIM FOR ME.

CIAO!

BIP.

RAAAAAAAAAAAAAAAA...

PWOF

MUMBLEGRUMBLE

CLANG.

OH NOT YOU...

HAVEN'T GOT THE TIME!

To The Blue Words Bookshop ...

Les Mots Bleus
Librairie Papeterie

♪DEGLIN!

THIS BOOK HERE!

MY DAUGHTER WROTE IT!

I'LL TAKE FOURTEEN

MUM?

MUM?

OH GREAT!

WHAT? WHO'S THAT?

OH, IT'S YOU

RWOF

31

ER NO, SHE'S NOT WITH ME, NO

I WISH SHE WAS

NO-THING

N...NOT AT MINA'S.

THAT OTHER GIRL

MARIWOTSIT

YE-ES?

I'LL PUT YOU THROUGH SHE'S JUST BACK FROM HER CAPOEIRA LESSON

DAHLING?

NOW WHAT?

WHO? LOU!

NO, NO, I...I...

OMYGOD!

WE HAD A ROW AND...

OMYGOD IT'S MY FAULT IF...

SHE'S PROBABLY KILLED HERSELF!

WOUAAHA!

MY LITTLE GIIRL, MY LITTLE BABY, I'M A TERRIBLE MOTHER!

WAIT. LET'S CALL THE POLICE

UM, BLONDE WITH, ER...

... HAIR LIKE THIS

HER CLOTHES?

UM...ER...

HOW CAN I DESCRIBE THEM?

IS THERE A PLACE SHE USUALLY GOES TO HIDE WHEN THINGS GO WRONG?

YES!

SHE'S NOT HERE

HO!

THERE

W...WELL, DOCTOR?

WHAT'S WRONG WITH HER?

FIRST OF ALL A RUNNY NOSE AND A RAGING FEVER, SHE'S GOT A NASTY DOSE OF FLU. DON'T WORRY, I'LL GIVE YOU A PRESCRIPTION FOR THAT...

TWO WEEKS' REST'LL DO IT!

BUT THERE'S SOMETHING ELSE...

SOMETHING ELSE?

SOMETHING I AM AFRAID I CAN'T HELP YOU WITH

A SERIOUS ADOLESCENT CRISIS

HUM.

THERE YOU GO

HERE'S MY BILL

A WHAT CRISIS?

HANG ON, ARE YOU REALLY CERTAIN ABOUT THE SECOND THING, CAN'T YOU PRESCRIBE SOMETHING?

PILLS, ANYTHING?

SNIFF

HEY.

HEY.

YOU REALLY DON'T SOUND TOO GOOD

SNIFF

NAH

SO... YOU CAN TALK NOW?

HAHAHA! WHAT RUBBISH, A TALKING CAT! HAHA! YOU'RE DELIRIOUS!

IT'S THE FEVER

AH, OK

SNIFF

WHAT'S HAPPENING? WHAT'S HAPPENING? I DIDN'T SEE IT COMING... ONLY YESTERDAY, SHE WAS A LITTLE GIRL, AND NOW, SUDDENLY...

A TEENAGER

I'M A TOTAL FAILURE, DAMMIT. SINCE SHE WAS A BABY, EVEN THOUGH I'VE TRIED TO GET IT RIGHT, TO ENSURE SHE LACKED FOR NOTHING, THAT SHE'S HAPPY ... AND...

I ER... I DON'T KNOW... BRINGING UP KIDS IS ER... LIKE STAR WARS... INITIATION AS A JEDI... YOU'RE A BIT LIKE OBI-WAN KENOBI—AND SHE'S LIKE ANAKIN

WHAT?

NO, HANG ON, YOU'RE MORE LIKE YODA, AND...

NO, I KNOW: ADOLESCENCE IS LIKE SUPERMAN BEING ADOPTED BY THE KENTS AND THEN WHEN HE HITS PUBERTY DISCOVERS HE'S ACTUALLY FROM KRYPTON. SO SUDDENLY HE DECIDES TO GO AND LIVE IN METROPOLIS ... ER ... NO ...

THERE'S NO COMPARISON ...

I DON'T THINK I'M REALLY THE BEST PERSON TO TALK TO ABOUT ADOLESCENCE AND THINGS, APART FROM MY STUPID COMPARISONS TO SUPERHEROES.... I MEAN... I THINK YOU'RE A BRILLIANT MUM. LOU'S SMART AND CREATIVE, BUT NOW SHE'S A TEENAGER, WHICH MEANS THERE ARE OBVIOUSLY THINGS YOU DON'T GET...

AND A ROAD SHE HAS TO GO DOWN ALONE.

I MEAN, I THINK

YOU'RE SWEET

BUT GOING BACK TO STAR WARS, I THINK I'M MORE LIKE QUI-GON JINN, DON'T YOU?

POC!

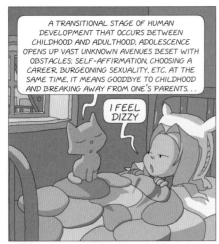
A TRANSITIONAL STAGE OF HUMAN DEVELOPMENT THAT OCCURS BETWEEN CHILDHOOD AND ADULTHOOD, ADOLESCENCE OPENS UP VAST UNKNOWN AVENUES BESET WITH OBSTACLES: SELF-AFFIRMATION, CHOOSING A CAREER, BURGEONING SEXUALITY, ETC. AT THE SAME TIME, IT MEANS GOODBYE TO CHILDHOOD AND BREAKING AWAY FROM ONE'S PARENTS...

I FEEL DIZZY

THE ADOLESCENT, ACCORDING TO GURU FRANÇOISE DOLTO, IS LIKE A LOBSTER WHICH, WHEN IT LOSES ITS SHELL, HAS TO GO AND HIDE UNDER THE ROCKS UNTIL IT HAS SECRETED A NEW SHELL. VULNERABLE TO ALL SORTS OF PROPOSITIONS, THE ADOLESCENT SOMETIMES TENDS TO COMPENSATE FOR HIS OR HER DEFENCELESSNESS BY SUDDENLY ADOPTING POSES ABRUPT MOOD SWINGS, OUTRAGEOUS, EVEN DEVIANT BEHAVIOUR...

SHUT UP

THE ADOLESCENT IS NOT ALONE IN THIS DIFFICULT TRANSITION. IT OFTEN LEADS TO A PROFOUND QUESTIONING OF THE ENTIRE FAMILY. SOME PEOPLE ARE NOT ABLE TO FIND SUFFICIENT INNER RESOURCES TO COPE WITH IT, WHICH CAN CREATE NUMEROUS DIFFICULTIES, WHICH SOCIETY TRIES TO RESOLVE WITH THE NECESSARY RESOURCES...

SHUT IT!

HEY.

HEY.

HERE, SOME SOUP AND YOUR MEDICINE

HAHAHAHA!

?

WHAT'S WRONG?

SOUP! HAHAHAHAHA!

YES, SOUP!

WHAT IS IT?

MUM?

YES?

CAN YOU ASK THE CAT TO STOP TALKING ALL THE TIME? I CAN'T GET TO SLEEP.

WHAT?

AND IT WOULD BE NICE IF YOU COULD PAINT MY ROOM WITH STRAWBERRY JAM

IT WOULD KEEP THE WILD ANIMALS AWAY

OH YEAH

YOU'VE STILL GOT A RAGING FEVER

YES, YES, ABSOLUTELY, I'VE WON THE DODDERSVALE GOLF TOURNAMENT THREE TIMES AND I . . .

AAAH! DEAR HORATIO HIGGINBOTTOM!

MY FAVOURITE PATIENT!

YOU KNOW, MY DEAR, DR HIGGINBOTTOM IS THE *REGIONAL EXPERT* ON CIRCULATORY PROBLEMS

GOODNESS!

YES, I....

DO YOU KNOW, ONLY LAST WEEK I HAD LYMPHATIC INFILTRATIONS IN MY CALVES, AND MY VARICOSE VEINS WERE TERRIBLY PAINFUL. WELL, DOCTOR HIGGINBOTTOM MASSAGED ME FOR THREE WHOLE HOURS, YOU SHOULD HAVE SEEN HIM . . .

IT WAS OOZING EVERYWHERE

MY HANDS WERE COVERED IN IT AND-

IS SOMETHING WRONG?

YOU'VE GONE ALL WHITE . .

SEE YOU SOON, HORATIO DEAR!

HE-HE-HE!

LOVELY CRISP LETTUCE! CRIIISP LETTUCES!

FRESH FISH ! FIIISH !

HMMM . . .

SCIIENCE-FICTION, *SCI-ENNNCE!*

COLLEGE GUY DEGRENNE

HEY

HEY

MAYBE YOU AND I SHOULD TALK TO EACH OTHER?

YEAH, COOL

NOT BECAUSE I LIKE YOU BUT IT'S BECAUSE OF LOU . . .

YEAH, SAME.

I MEAN, YOU KNOW, HER SORT OF RUNNING AWAY AND ALL THAT . . .

HER MUM CALLED ME TOO, YEAH . .

I'M GOING TO HER PLACE AT 6

I'VE GOT SOME NOTES FOR HER, I'LL COME WITH YOU . . .

I'LL COME TOO

MINA!

AND ER... MARIWOTSIT...

AND ER...

HELLO

I DON'T KNOW YOU, DO I?

RIGHT ER....
.IT'S THAT WAY, YOU KNOW...

I'LL LEAVE YOU TO IT

BY THE WAY, WHILE YOU'RE HERE . . .

DO ANY OF YOU KNOW ANYTHING ABOUT ADOLESCENCE. . .?

'COS I'M OUT OF MY DEPTH HERE

WHY ARE YOU ALL STARING AT ME LIKE THAT?

CHILL, OK, I'M NOT DYING!

YEAH, RIGHT, IT'S JUST...

I MEAN...

YEAH, WE FEEL .LIKE IT'S OUR FAULT THAT...

THAT WHAT?

THAT, LIKE, YOU'RE. . .

I MEAN, THAT YOU'RE NOT WELL AND STUFF . . .

COS I DID YOUR HEAD IN WITH MY TALKING AND . . .

BECAUSE I'M SUCH A HORRIBLE PERSON. . .

ARE YOU CRAZY OR WHAT?

HEY GIRLS, IT'S TOTALLY NOT YOUR FAULT, YOU'RE TALKING CRAP!

ALL THE SAME, YOU ARE A HORRIBLE PERSON, AND YES, YOU DID MY HEAD IN, BUT THAT'S GOT NOTHING TO DO WITH IT, IT'S JUST...

I DON'T KNOW HOW TO EXPLAIN...

I KIND OF FREAKED OUT . . .

A GREAT BIG EMPTINESS . I FEEL A LOT BETTER NOW BUT IT WAS LIKE I WANTED TO CRY ALL THE TIME . . .

I DUNNO...

AS IF I WAS EXPECTING SOMETHING TO HAPPEN...

AND THEN NOTHING

NOTHING AT ALL ...

NOTHING BUT A SORT OF AGONISING EMPTINESS . .

I MEAN...

I DON'T KNOW IF YOU UNDERSTAND ME...

YEAH, I KNOW EXACTLY WHAT YOU MEAN...

YUK!

AND WHAT DID PSYCHOANALYST FRANÇOISE DOLTO SAY ABOUT PEOPLE WHO LICK THEIR BOTTOMS CLEAN?

MEEOW

I'M BETTER!

DO YOU WANT TO TALK ABOUT UM...

WHAT?

THIS ADOLESCENCE BUSINESS...

THERE ARE SOME THINGS WE SHOULD TALK ABOUT, MAYBE

ER YES. NO... I DON'T KNOW WHAT HAPPENED... ANYWAY, I THINK I'M BETTER NOW.

I'M SUPPOSED TO TELL YOU REASSURING STUFF, THAT'S WHAT PARENTS ARE MEANT TO DO, I THINK.. .BUT TO BE HONEST I CAN'T THINK OF ANYTHING...

ALL I CAN REMEMBER IS THAT I WAS LIKE THAT AT YOUR AGE...

I REMEMBER THAT TIME VERY CLEARLY...

THE ONLY THING I FEEL CAPABLE OF DOING IS CONTINUING TO LOVE YOU VERY MUCH...

BESIDES, THERE'S NO MAGIC FORMULA TO MAKE EVERYTHING ALL RIGHT. NO TRUTH, I THINK. ALL THIS UNCERTAINTY... I STILL HAVEN'T FOUND THE ANSWER...

MAYBE IT'S BETTER NOT TO ANSWER.

THAT'S FINE WITH ME...

THIS MIGHT COME IN USEFUL

43

PL PFFF!

MY BANK ACCOUNT!

IN CREDIT!

MY BOOK...

ROYALTIES...

YEEEHAA!

RENT!

FMAK!

YEEHAA!

YOU KNOW I'M SO HAPPY THAT MARY-EMILY'S GOT SOME LITTLE FRIENDS AT LAST...

SHE'S SUCH A SOLITARY CHILD, I...

OH! YOU DRINK IT STRAIGHT OUT OF THE BOTTLE

TELL ME...I'VE JUST HAD AN IDEA... EVERY YEAR WE RENT A BIG VILLA BY THE SEA. MAYBE ALL FOUR OF YOU WOULD LIKE TO COME?

THERE'S PLENTY OF ROOM AND A HUUUGE SWIMMING POOL!

WOOOHA MUM, SHUT UP! YOU'RE SOOO EMBARRASSING...

ALL FOUR OF US?

A SWIMMING POOL?

BY THE SEA?

SAY YES! SAY YES! SAY YES! SAY YES!

PLIZ, ON MY MOTHER'S LIFE!

I AM YOUR MUM

PLIZ! PLIZ! PLIZ! PLIZ! PLIZ! PLIZ! PLIZ!

YEAH, WELL MAYBE IT'S OK...

PLIZ!
PLIZ!
PLIZ!
PLIZ!

LISTEN, I DON'T KNOW...THIS SUMMER I'LL BE TOURING ALL OVER THE PLACE DOING BOOK SIGNINGS SO...

PLIZ!
PLIZ!
PLIZ!
PLIZ!

WE'LL SEE...IT DEPENDS ON WHY YOU WANT TO GO, I...

PLIZ!
PLIZ!
PLIZ!
PLIZ!
PLIZ!
PLIZ!

RIGHT, OK THEN, BUT...

YES!

WOOHOO!

HIHIHI!

WHAT?

NOTHING!

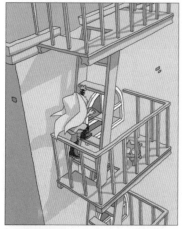

CLIC!

DEAR PAUL

MAry-EMily

Actually, that look means:
" Please love me."

Mary-Emily, there's a girl
with REALLY MAJOR problems.
For one, her bedroom is so big
that once she got lost in it.

Yeah, there's
staff like that
you know...

It Sooo makes you
want to rebel,
you know

NOTE: Actually, She's good fun. Just from
time to time you have to tell her to:
S H U T   U P !
and then she's normal for a few hours

K-rine

At first, me and K-rine,
we didn't exactly hit it off.
And then, in the end, we spent
quite a lot of time talking
and.... well anyway, now
she's a friend.

Right, anyway, we'd better
get on well, seeing as we're all
going on HOLIDAY together
this summer!
Can't
WAIT!

A sensitive creature is hidden inside
this tracksuit. Can you find her?